ANIMAL TEETH

ANIMAL TEETH

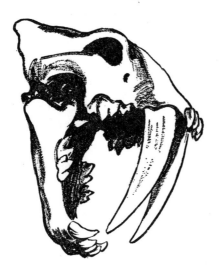

written and illustrated by
GEORGE F. MASON

William Morrow and Company
New York 1965

CONTENTS

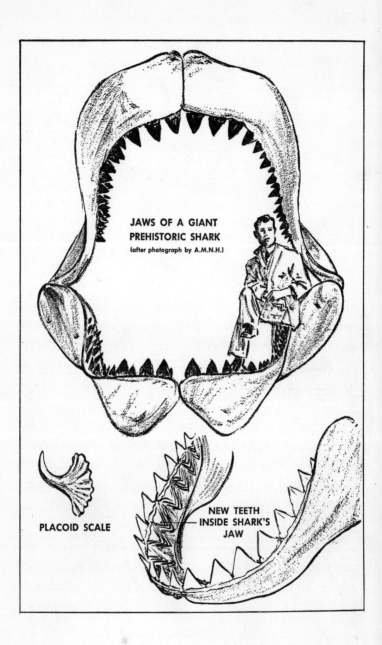

JAWS OF A GIANT
PREHISTORIC SHARK
(after photograph by A.M.N.H.)

PLACOID SCALE

NEW TEETH
INSIDE SHARK'S
JAW

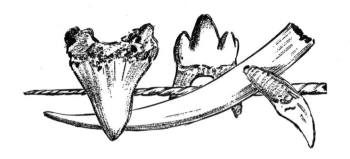

HOW TEETH GROW

My introduction to the peculiarities of animal teeth began several years ago in a natural history museum when I visited a hall in which a group of men were at work on a fossil fish exhibit. They were setting up for display a reconstruction of the open jaws, measuring at least nine feet across, of an enormous extinct species of shark. Rows of large sharply pointed teeth were embedded in plaster of Paris forms, which took the place of the missing upper and lower jaws of the original fish. Although the jaws were made of plaster, the teeth were those of a shark that lived three hundred million years ago.

Upon closely examining one of the teeth, I was surprised to find it in almost perfect condition. I asked how it was possible for teeth to remain in such a fine state of preservation after being buried in the earth for three hundred million years. One of the men told me that the teeth might not have lasted as long in their natural state, but these were fossilized so completely that they would last forever. He went on to explain how parts of prehistoric plants and animals become fossilized by absorbing minerals that change the original plant or animal matter to a mineralized state. All the pulp and enamel of the shark's teeth had been changed to indestructible rock-like matter, yet the original form of the teeth remained unchanged in the process.

Shortly after seeing the fossil shark teeth, I examined the mounted specimen of a man-eating shark to find out if its teeth were similar to those of its ancient ancestor. Although they were keener-edged, much smaller and more numerous, the man-eater's teeth closely resembled those of the prehistoric fish. Directly behind every front tooth lies a row of additional teeth. The teeth lie flat and overlap one another on the inside of the shark's jaws. They are replacements for front ones occasionally lost or broken off during the shark's lifetime. Shortly after a front tooth is lost, a new one gradually grows forward and moves into its place. From this endless supply of spare teeth the shark gets new ones, when needed, as long as it lives. With but a few exceptions, the teeth of all fish are constantly renewed throughout life.

Strange as it may seem, a shark hasn't a bone in

its body. Its inner skeleton is composed of a material called cartilage, which is much softer than bone. Its skin, however, is covered with placoid scales, which are harder than bone and form an outer skeleton. A placoid scale consists of a bony plate with a spine in the center. The spine is composed of ivory, called dentine, and is covered with enamel similar to that covering a tooth. It is directed backward, forming a hook. Along the jaw some of the scales have become modified to function as teeth.

The world's largest living fish is the whale shark, which is bigger than the prehistoric giants that possessed such enormous jaws and teeth. It may grow to a length of sixty feet, yet this gigantic member of the ferocious shark family is one of the most harmless creatures in the ocean. Its food consists of small organisms filtered out of the water by its gills. It has no known enemies and even lacks the ability to put up a fight when captured by man. This unusual fish has about three thousand teeth in each jaw, but they are only an eighth of an inch long!

This interesting information about sharks' teeth led me to investigate the various kinds of teeth in other animals' jaws, and I found out that mammal teeth are different from those of fish in structure and growth. Mammal teeth are formed by skin cells. The development begins even before birth when the outer layer of skin dips down into the deeper skin and thickens. Then small blood vessels enter the base

9

of the thickening mass, forming a knot and supplying nourishment. The base of the tooth germ becomes cone-shaped, and the outer layer takes on the form of a cap. Meanwhile, cells within the cap begin to produce enamel, the hardest tissue of the body. Also at this stage of development, the outer layer of cells produce a threadlike outgrowth that forms dentine. It grows from the top toward the base of the tooth and from the outside inward. As the top and sides of the tooth thicken, a shrinking takes place in the central cone, or pulp, which contains the blood vessels, nerves, and living dentine cells. As the roots develop, the tooth begins to lose its broad connection with the tissue of the jaw; when mature, there is little more than a tiny, red thread of life running halfway up the center of the tooth. While this shrinkage is typical in the development of most teeth, it does not occur in the development of ever-growing teeth, such as the incisors of rodents and elephants, or the canine tusks of pigs and walruses. These teeth have open roots that contain a large pulp and broad supply lines for bringing nourishment from the body. They are frequently called rootless to distinguish them from typical teeth that have one or more roots.

As a tooth develops the surrounding tissue becomes compressed and forms a capsule. Bony matter known as cementum forms around the roots and sometimes parts of the crown, or top of the tooth. In

10

simple teeth like ours and those of the flesheaters, the layer of cementum covering the crown is so thin it is worn away almost the first time the teeth are used for chewing. It is much thicker below the gum line where the enamel cap stops, however, and it helps to strengthen the roots of the tooth.

To describe the teeth of every known animal would be a tremendous task, therefore I shall only discuss the teeth that interest me for one reason or another and point out some of the structural differences of various kinds of teeth in the mouths of mammals, fish, reptiles, and amphibians.

MAMMAL TEETH

Mammals are animals that nourish their young with milk. At some period in their existence, all mammals bear a coat of hair, though some, like whales and human beings, lose most of it before birth. Almost all adult mammals have teeth, and their dental equipment differs from that of fishes, amphibians, and reptiles in several ways. Their teeth are fewer, and in any species the number is characteristic and almost never varies.

Mammal teeth are set in sockets. They are separated from the bone surrounding them by a fine membrane of softer tissue and never fuse with the jaw as those of most reptiles do. While the teeth in front of a mammal's mouth are single-rooted, the cheek teeth, or molars, usually have two, three, or many roots implanted in distinct sockets in the jaw.

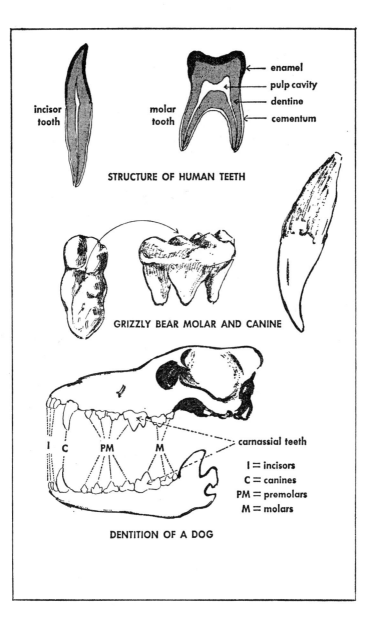

incisor tooth

molar tooth

enamel
pulp cavity
dentine
cementum

STRUCTURE OF HUMAN TEETH

GRIZZLY BEAR MOLAR AND CANINE

I   C   PM   M

carnassial teeth

I = incisors
C = canines
PM = premolars
M = molars

DENTITION OF A DOG

The single-rooted tooth is fastened to the jaw as a carrot is fastened to the earth, while the many-rooted tooth resembles a tree in its attachments.

Mammals have two or more kinds of teeth, serving different needs. They also have only two sets of teeth: the temporary milk teeth, or baby teeth, shed before full growth, and the permanent set. Reptiles and fish, on the other hand, usually have a continuous supply of teeth so that injured or worn-out ones are replaced by new teeth when needed. Mammals are less fortunate in this respect, and a broken incisor tooth frequently means certain death for them.

A small number of mammals have a single set of teeth, and several shed their milk teeth before or soon after birth. Whalebone whales and a few land mammals have no teeth, although they may have had rudimentary teeth that were shed at an early stage of their development.

Mammal teeth are divided into four distinct groups. In one side of the upper jaw of a dog, for example, there are three simple teeth imbedded in sockets of the front bone. They are called incisors. Behind them and separated by a gap there is a single tooth with a cone-shaped crown. This tooth is the tusk, or canine tooth, and in most carnivorous animals it is very large. Behind the canine come the cheek teeth, usually six in number. They have complicated crowns, and, except for the first, they are attached to the jaw with two or more roots.

The second, third, and fourth cheek teeth of a dog are the successors of milk teeth and are known as premolars. The last two cheek teeth, which have no temporary milk teeth preceding them, are the true molars. If possible, look into a young puppy's mouth and count the milk teeth in its upper jaw. You will probably find fourteen, all of which are shed when the second, or permanent, teeth grow in. The permanent teeth of the upper jaw, of which there are twenty in all, appear after the puppy is about three months old.

Most mammals that have teeth of different kinds, except for the pouched animals, never have more than three incisors, one canine, four premolars, and three molars on either side of each jaw.

Any complete description of a mammal includes a record of its teeth. For convenience and accuracy its dentition is expressed in a graphic formula that clearly shows the number and identity of the teeth in each half of the upper and lower jaws. The incisors are indicated by the letter I, the canines by C, the premolars by P, and the molars by M. Using figures above and below a line to represent the number of teeth in the upper and lower half of each jaw, we may express the formula for an adult dog's teeth as $I\frac{3}{3}$, $C\frac{1}{1}$, $P\frac{4}{4}$, $M\frac{2}{3} = 21$. The total adds up to ten in half of the upper jaw and eleven in half of the lower. By doubling these numbers, one gets the

16

entire number of teeth in a dog's mouth—forty-two.

The teeth of a mammal reveal many things about the kind of food it eats, for each species has one or more kinds of teeth for capturing, killing, chewing, grinding, or crushing the food on which it lives. The eating habits of mammals can be divided into five principal classes: omnivorous (eat everything), insectivorous (eat insects), carnivorous (eat meat), piscivorous (eat fish), and herbivorous (eat plants). There are also toothless or near toothless mammals that feed principally on a diet of insects, although they are not classed as insectivores.

Some mammals whose eating habits require little or no use of teeth do not have front teeth and cheek teeth, or their cheek teeth are peculiar to their kind. They belong in the order edentates, which means *tooth out* in Latin. Included in the order are anteaters, sloths, and armadillos, all found in South America. The anteater's jaws are entirely toothless while the sloths and armadillos have cheek teeth composed of ivory and cementum without any trace of enamel. Having no distinct roots, these teeth are open-rooted and grow continuously like the incisors of a rodent.

OMNIVOROUS MAMMALS

The teeth of omnivorous mammals are shaped somewhat like our own except for the canines. These

17

teeth are larger, so they may be used for fighting or digging up the ground in search of food, as a pig uses its tusks. The molars are broad and have low, rounded cusps, or points, on the crown. The upper cusps fit in between the lower cusps, forming an efficient crushing machine. As a rule, the premolars are similar, but have fewer cusps. While the molar and premolar teeth are not highly specialized for either grinding or shearing, they are adequately suited for chewing the various kinds of food eaten by omnivorous animals. Pigs, bears, and many mice, as well as most monkeys and apes, have premolar and molar teeth of this general type. Of these animals, the apes have teeth most similar to ours, except for their larger canine teeth. Also, their cheek teeth form a nearly straight line while human cheek teeth are set in a slightly curving line.

The formula for an ape's dentition is the same as the one for ours:

$$I\frac{2}{2}, \ C\frac{1}{1}, \ P\frac{2}{2}, \ M\frac{3}{3} \ = \ 16 \times 2 \ = \ 32$$

Since man is biologically a mammal, a few words about the teeth of human beings are not out of place in this chapter. In spite of the array of flashing teeth revealed on the smiling faces of models, actors, and thousands of faces pictured in advertisements, our teeth are undoubtedly the most vulnerable to decay of any in the animal world. Why has it become necessary for almost every civilized human being to have

18

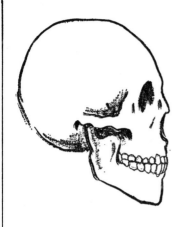

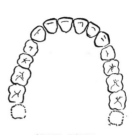

UPPER TEETH
OF A MAN

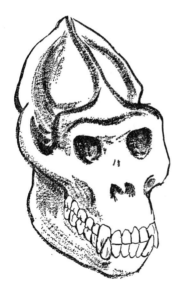

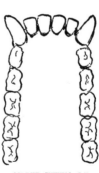

UPPER TEETH OF
A GORILLA

the frequent services of a dentist in order to keep his or her teeth in good condition? And in spite of the best of care, isn't it often necessary to remove poor teeth and replace them with bridgework or dentures?

It is true that the teeth of wild animals are occasionally damaged by excessive wear, injury, or decay, but overall they are likely to remain in fair condition during an animal's life-span. What causes our teeth to decay so often while those of almost all wild animals do not?

The answer may be faulty diet. One man who was convinced that the food we now eat is the cause of most of our dental troubles is the late famous explorer-anthropologist Vilhjalmur Stefansson. I became acquainted with Mr. Stefansson several years ago when seeking his advice on a proposed trip to the Arctic Circle. He was more than generous and kind in helping me with my plans, and as I was preparing to leave, he presented me with an autographed copy of his latest book, *Not by Bread Alone.* In this interesting and exciting book I found several pages devoted to the effect of diet on the condition of human teeth.

Mr. Stefansson's book tells how he examined the teeth in hundreds of skulls of primitive human beings without finding any evidence of tooth decay. The accuracy of his observation can be checked by anyone who studies the same skull collections in the

anthropological departments of Harvard University
and the American Museum of Natural History.

Since the best evidence available indicates that
the food of these primitive people was almost entirely meat, Mr. Stefansson reasoned that the meat
diet was responsible for the absence of cavities in
their teeth. Further studies of the teeth belonging
to primitive people who ate foods such as sugar,
flour, and cereals revealed the presence of tooth decay. By comparing the condition of the teeth in the
skulls of meat eaters with those of people known to
have had a mixed diet, Mr. Stefansson concluded
that man's diet has a pronounced effect on the condition of his teeth.

Today there may be in remote parts of the world
a few primitive races of human beings whose main
food is meat, but most of the human race now sub-
sists on a mixed diet. It cannot be otherwise, for
populations have increased so much that there
would not be enough food to go around if everyone
depended on meat alone. Since we cannot suddenly
change to a diet of meat and eliminate sugars and
starches entirely in the attempt to improve the condition of our teeth, we can be thankful that we have
doctors and dentists to repair the damage caused
by eating modern foods. Without the dentist's expert services there would be very few smiling faces
to admire.

Judging from Mr. Stefansson's theories about the

absence of tooth decay among primitive, meat-eating people, I think man must have evolved originally as a carnivore. Then as he advanced to a civilized state he became omnivorous. Now he eats anything that tastes good, digests easily, and supplies nourishment. Our so-called balanced diet keeps us healthy, but it may affect the metabolism of the human body in a way that weakens the resistance of human teeth to decay. A meat diet is not necessary to prevent tooth decay in all mammals, such as those, like cows, that have always been plant eaters, but there is evidence that it would be better for human teeth.

Since it seems that evolution tends to eliminate useless teeth, is it not possible that teeth may eventually disappear from human jaws? Primitive people used their teeth constantly, but today our diet of soft foods gives us little opportunity to chew rough and tough materials. For evolution to bring about such an extreme change in human dentition would require millions of years, however, so human beings need not worry about becoming toothless in the near future.

INSECTIVOROUS (INSECT-EATING) MAMMALS

Teeth suited to insect-eating habits are of various types. The cheek teeth are squarish, with sharp

cusps and edges that shear past each other somewhat like the teeth in the gears of a machine. Those
of the shrews and bats usually have W patterns on
the crown both above and below, although the pattern of the crown of the last upper molar is com-
monly N- or even V-shaped. These teeth are able to
chop up the hard bodies of insects. The front teeth
of shrews are long and project forward like a pair
of forceps, excellent for seizing quick-moving small
insects. They are also deadly weapons when the
shrew attacks larger animals, such as mice. It is interesting to note that the skunk, which feeds largely
on insects although its teeth are distributed like
those of a carnivore, has broad, crushing cheek
teeth very much like the teeth of true insectivores.
Also, their upper incisors meet their lower incisors
and these small vertical teeth can hold the tiniest
insect.

Bats have strange eating habits. Some are insect
eaters, although they are not classed as insectivores.
Others eat only fruit, and the vampire bat has the
distinction of being the one tropical American mammal that feeds on blood alone. Insect-eating bats
have cheek teeth with a number of sharp cusps,
which make them suitable for holding and cutting
up tough insect bodies. The cheek teeth of fruit-
eating bats, however, are smooth and without cusps.
The blood-sucking vampires have a remarkable pair
of incisor teeth admirably designed for the work

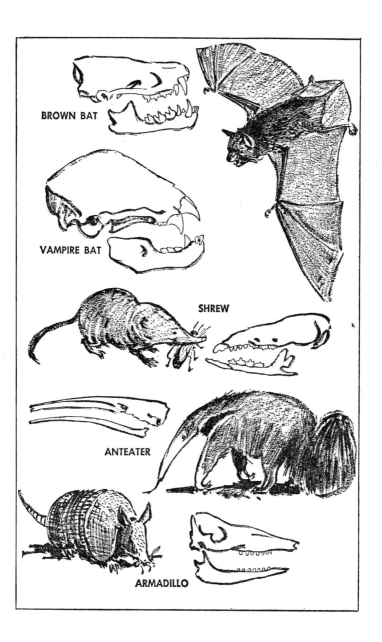

BROWN BAT

VAMPIRE BAT

SHREW

ANTEATER

ARMADILLO

they do. The upper incisors and the canines are triangular and project forward. Their edges and tip are razor sharp and enable the bat to cut skin so skillfully that the sleeping victim of this operation seldom awakens. The vampire then laps up the flowing blood from the incision as a cat laps milk. It has little or no use for its cheek teeth, which are very small and weak.

CARNIVOROUS (FLESH-EATING) MAMMALS

Mammals such as cats, dogs, bears, hyenas, weasels, foxes, and others, together with aquatic seals and walruses, are classified in the order of carnivores, or flesh eaters. Their teeth are generally large and well developed, and they always have incisors, tusks or fangs (canines), and cheek teeth. As a general rule, there are never more than three incisors on each side of the upper and lower jaws. (Marsupial carnivores are exceptions.) The canines are large, adapted for seizing prey or fighting. There is a great deal of variation in the structure of the cheek teeth among the different families in the order, but usually the back teeth are sharp, especially the last upper premolar and the first lower molar, which shear past each other with scissorlike action. These teeth are called carnassial teeth, and their large slicing blades cut flesh into sizes that can be conveniently swallowed.

Carnassial teeth reach their highest development in members of the cat family. If you give a cat a sizable piece of meat or fish to eat, you can see how it uses its carnassial teeth to slice the food. Cats are unable to move their jaws sideways in a grinding action, as deers or cows chew, so they often turn their heads sideways as they bite down on their food. Although cats have a total of twelve or fourteen cheek teeth, only ten or twelve are useful, for the two upper molars are too small to be of any use in cutting up flesh. The formula for the cat's dentition is:

$$I\frac{3}{3}, \ C\frac{1}{1}, \ P\frac{3 \text{ or } 2}{2}, \ M\frac{1}{1} \ = \ 14 \text{ or } 15 \times 2 \ = \ 28 \text{ or } 30.$$

The general shape and structure of the teeth are more or less the same among all present-day cats, but in prehistoric times there was a ferocious cat with enormously long canine teeth in its upper jaw. When scientists discovered the remains of these cats in tar pits, they found several skulls with well-preserved teeth. The upper fangs projected downward far below the lower jaw and formed an obstruction that must have prevented the cat from biting in the ordinary manner. It is believed that such teeth were useful only as weapons for killing other animals, although they must have presented a problem afterward when the cat was eating the flesh of its prey.

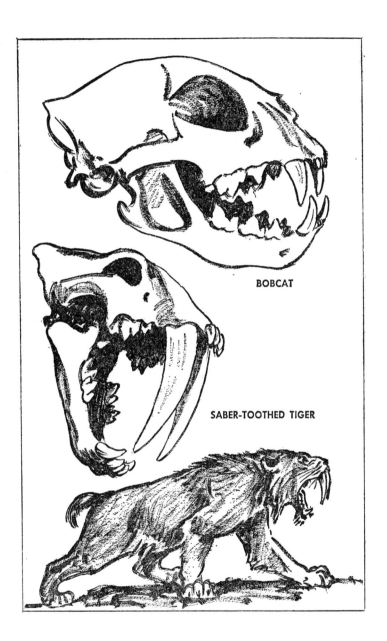

BOBCAT

SABER-TOOTHED TIGER

The remains of these cats, which became extinct over fifty thousand years ago, are exhibited in several museums throughout the world. They are identified as saber-toothed tigers. The walrus is the only living carnivore that has a pair of long canine teeth larger than those of the prehistoric saber-toothed tiger.

Among all present-day carnivores the much-despised African spotted hyena has the most powerful jaws and teeth. Its strong, conical premolars, strengthened by small cusps on the front and rear of their base, form crushing teeth of terrific power. With them a hyena is capable of crushing the large shinbones of a buffalo as easily as a dog crushes a chicken bone. The spotted hyena is cowardly, yet it is one of the few wild animals that will attack, kill, and eat a sick or injured human being.

PISCIVOROUS (FISH-EATING) MAMMALS

Mammals that feed primarily on fish usually have sharp teeth that curve backward, called recurved teeth, or a large number of sharp-pointed, needle-like teeth for holding their prey. Since most of these animals swallow their food whole, the cheek teeth are not adapted for grinding or cutting. Some toothed seals and whales have recurved teeth, and the leopard seal's cheek teeth have three sharp cusps on the crown of each tooth. These teeth are called tricuspid.

The Weddell seal of the south polar regions has entirely different teeth. These hardy animals live under ice that in the winter may freeze to a thickness of eight feet. With their strong teeth they are able to rasp breathing holes to the surface. The seal seeks out one of the huge cracks that occur when the ice contracts, comes up inside the crack, and chews through the ice that forms over it. Their strong, peg-like teeth project forward, enabling the seal to use them like a drill, twisting and swinging its head, with the mouth wide open, until it breaks through several inches of ice in a short time.

The male narwhal has an extraordinary spirally twisted tusk projecting from one side of its upper jaw. Apart from a few rudimentary teeth, the male narwhal has no others, and the female is practically toothless. The growth and structure of the tusks are interesting, for though two tusks grow within the male's skull, only one develops, and it is almost always the one on the left side. The opposite tusk remains concealed within the jawbone. The long tusk often attains a length of seven or eight feet. It is composed of ivory, and its spiral twist always runs from left to right. Since the narwhal feeds on small fish and crustaceans, which are swallowed whole, it probably uses its tusk as a weapon instead of a feeding tool.

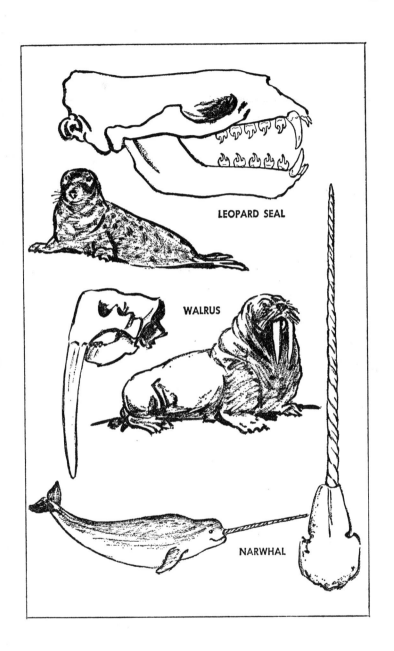

LEOPARD SEAL

WALRUS

NARWHAL

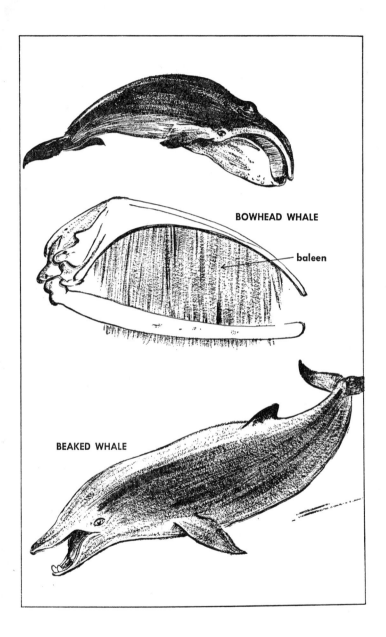

BOWHEAD WHALE

baleen

BEAKED WHALE

Beaked whales generally have only one or two pairs of teeth near the tip of their lower jaw. The teeth of one species of these whales are extraordinary, however, for they can be raised or lowered at will. The teeth, set in cartilaginous sacs, are moved up or down in their socket by muscular action.

The jaws of dolphins and porpoises are lined with a large number of teeth, many species having more than a hundred teeth in all.

The toothless whales live on quantities of plankton and small sea life, which they swallow by the bushel. Instead of teeth they have baleen, or whalebone, in their jaws, which acts like a sieve, retaining food while the whale expels water from its mouth.

HERBIVOROUS
(GRASS- AND PLANT-EATING) MAMMALS

The teeth of plant eaters, especially those that feed largely on grass, are quite different from the teeth of other mammals. Animals that feed entirely on grass and leaves must chew their food thoroughly to extract all its nourishment, since it is digested mostly by enzymes present in the mouth rather than by stomach juices. Their cheek teeth are specialized to do this work successfully. The molar teeth are large and have complicated ridges of hard enamel that form a definite pattern on the grinding surfaces as the teeth are worn down. By carefully examining the grinding teeth of a horse, it is possible to distinguish the three substances of which they are composed. If the tooth is not worn by use, the cap and sides will be covered with the grayish white cement of bony tissue. Cement fills the deep pockets of the tooth also. On a worn tooth, where the top layer of cement is worn away, a thick layer of enamel can be seen. The enamel usually forms a folding pattern and is supported by surrounding masses of ivory, or dentine. It wears away more slowly than the softer ivory, leaving a pattern of raised enamel ridges.

Plant-eating mammals, especially those that chew their cud, also have large cheek teeth with very high crowns. Because they chew their food twice, once before swallowing and again when they bring it up from the stomach, the cud-chewing mammals give their cheek teeth a tremendous amount of wear. Grass contains hard, abrasive silica in its fibers, and usually there is some sand or dust on plants growing close to the ground. When an animal chews great quantities of grass each day, its cheek teeth wear down. Possibly the life-span of such a mammal is determined largely by the lasting qualities of its teeth.

The cheek teeth of horses wear flat on the grinding surface. Those of deer, antelope, and bison have a crescent pattern of high and low ridges of enamel. As the animal moves its jaws from side to side, it

PATTERN OF ENAMEL ON CROWN OF A HORSE'S MOLAR

MOLAR TOOTH OF A HORSE

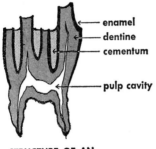

enamel
dentine
cementum

pulp cavity

STRUCTURE OF AN OX'S MOLAR

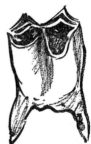

MOLAR TOOTH OF A DEER

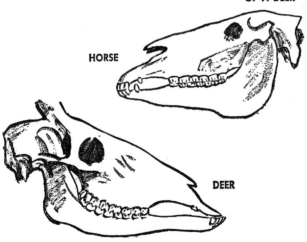

HORSE

DEER

shreds and grinds its food between the sharp, angular surface of its teeth.

The upper canine teeth are generally missing among the grass eaters, but the wapiti stag has two small canines composed of pure ivory. Long ago these ivory canines were highly prized by some Indian tribes, who used them as ornaments on their buckskin clothing. Today they are still sought after by some manufacturers of watch charms and club emblems. The males of several species of Asiatic deer have long, daggerlike upper canines, which they use in fighting.

Members of the cow and deer families have a full set of lower incisors while the upper incisors are replaced by a horny pad. They can grip grass and leaves firmly between the teeth and pad, and then tear them off by a quick jerk of the head. Because of the lack of upper incisors, these animals never bite human beings or each other. On the other hand, horses have powerful upper as well as lower incisors and use them in fighting each other. If a horse should be bad-tempered, it can give its master a serious bite.

Years ago when horses were more common than they are today, I remember seeing men examine the teeth of horses they were considering buying or trading. An expert horse trader could learn the age of a horse by noting the condition of the animal's teeth, especially the incisor teeth. When the first in-

41

cisor teeth appear in a colt's jaws they are covered with enamel, which dips inward forming a pit on the crown of each tooth. In a year or two the enamel on the high ridges surrounding the pit wears away, leaving the pit surrounded by a ring of enamel. When new incisors replace the milk teeth they, too, show a pit, or mark, as it is called. As the teeth are worn down by use, the pit becomes shallower until, eventually, it disappears. As a rule, the mark wears off the first incisor of the lower jaw at six years, the second incisor at seven years, and the third incisor at eight years. The upper incisors usually maintain the mark about two years longer than those in the lower jaw. After the age of ten or so, when the marks are worn away from all the incisors, there is no further indication of the horse's exact age. Nevertheless, the extent to which the teeth are worn down may give a hint in estimating the probable age of an old horse.

Horses and cattle move their jaws from side to side, but elephants move their jaws back and forth when chewing. The elephant's cheek teeth are the largest of all mammal grinding teeth and their structure and growth are interesting in many respects. A young elephant has six cheek teeth on either side of the upper and lower jaws, but never more than two of them are exposed at one time. When one wears out, the next tooth in back appears. This process is

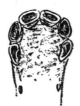

one month   three years   six years

HORSE'S UPPER INCISORS AND TUSKS

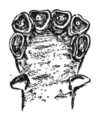
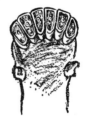

eight years   fifteen years   thirty years

**CROSS SECTION OF AN INCISOR
TOOTH WORN DOWN TO
SHOW THE MARK**

THE MARK

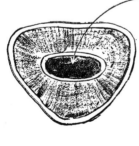
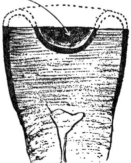

repeated until old age when only one last tooth remains.

These enormous teeth are unlike those of any other mammal. The crown, which makes a good grinding surface, is composed of a series of enamel ridges in the form of elongated ellipses running transversely across the tooth. The material inside the borders of the enamel ellipse is ivory, and the substance surrounding the enamel is cement. As the upper and lower cheek teeth wear down, the crowns form slightly concave or convex surfaces. The crowns do not become smooth, because of differences in the hardness of the enamel, ivory and cement. The enamel, harder than ivory and cement, wears away more slowly than the other materials and, therefore, creates a series of raised enamel cutting edges across the crown.

It seems incredible that an elephant's tusk is actually a modified upper incisor tooth, and that aside from the two tusks there are no other teeth in the front of an elephant's mouth. An elephant is born with a pair of milk tusks, which are shed at a very early age. The permanent tusks have open roots, and they continue to grow throughout the life of the elephant like all open-rooted teeth. During the early stages of their growth the tusks are tipped with enamel, but it soon wears off, and then they consist of ivory alone. Elephant ivory can be distinguished from other kinds or imitations by the spiral pattern visible in a cross section of it.

Some of the elephantlike animals that existed thousands of years ago had tremendous tusks. They grew in graceful curves and probably served little purpose other than decoration. Modern elephants use their tusks more as tools for digging and for lifting heavy burdens than as weapons, though they probably use them when fighting among themselves. The elephants trained to handle heavy teakwood logs in India are those with long, strong tusks. The weight of the log rests on the tusks while the elephant's trunk is used like a binding rope to hold the log in place when it is being carried.

In most instances tusks are useful to an animal, yet it is difficult to understand the real usefulness of such abnormal tusks as those of the Malayan wild pig called a babirusa. The males have long, scimitar-shaped tusks. Unlike other wild pigs, whose upper canines curve outward and upward beneath the upper lip, the babirusa's upper tusks penetrate upward through the skin of the snout and curve backward until they reach the forehead near the eyes. Since the point of these tusks rests too close to the pig's skull to be of any use for fighting or digging, they seem to have no function other than decoration. It is also possible that they may be of some use in protecting the boar's eyes when fighting.

Pigs' tusks are ever-growing canines with open

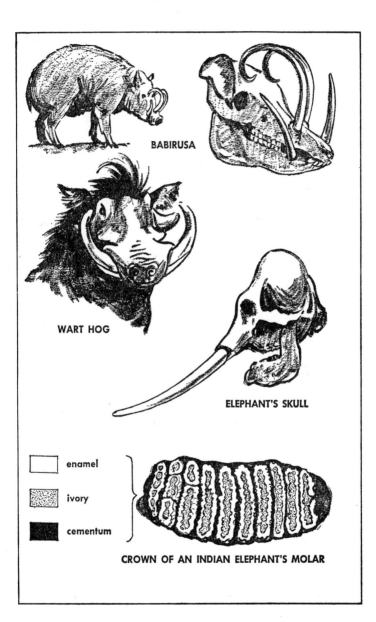

BABIRUSA

WART HOG

ELEPHANT'S SKULL

enamel

ivory

cementum

CROWN OF AN INDIAN ELEPHANT'S MOLAR

roots. Among wild swine, the African wart hog has the largest tusks. The lower ones, kept sharp by rubbing against the sides of the larger, upper tusks, are the weapons that do the most damage to the pig's adversary when fighting. The enormous upper tusks look like frightful weapons, but they are valuable to the pig chiefly as digging tools. The collared peccary is the only wild pig native to America. While its tusks are relatively small compared with those of the wart hogs, the peccary is dangerous when provoked and can inflict severe wounds with its dagger-like tusks.

A pig's cheek teeth are quite different from those of the cud-chewing animals. They are strong and rather low-crowned, enabling the pig to crush the hard shells of nuts and to grind up tough roots and tubers. The last molar at both ends of each jaw is greatly elongated.

Even though it is an enormous animal with a big appetite, the hippopotamus is a popular resident in many zoological gardens. In captivity the hippo soon learns to beg for handouts by opening his huge, cavernous mouth and waiting patiently for people to toss peanuts and popcorn into it. Everyone who looks into a hippo's open mouth is usually greatly impressed by the odd display of teeth and tusks protruding from its jaws.

The tusks (canines) and incisors are composed of pure white ivory surrounded by a thick layer of enamel, except for the points of the curved lower tusks, which rub against the upper tusks and wear down to the ivory. Two incisors projecting down from the upper jaw look like long, pointed pegs. The incisors and tusks are ever-growing and do not form roots. The cheek teeth are broad with grinding surfaces good for chewing grass and water plants, which are the chief foods eaten by wild hippos.

A museum friend once gave me some hippo tusks from which I carved several small objects to attach to chains and pins. An ivory fish, which I carved for my wife, has changed from pure white to a warm cream color after being worn as a pendant for several years. The ivory, which is harder than elephant ivory, used to be an important material in making artificial teeth for human beings. According to history, George Washington wore dentures made of ivory. Perhaps the source of his artificial teeth was the jaw of a hippopotamus!

RODENTS

Rodents are also plant eaters, but their teeth are distinctive and need to be discussed separately. Most of them are small animals, such as squirrels, woodchucks, porcupines, rats, mice, and gophers; the largest in North America is the beaver. They are all distinguished by two unusually sharp, continuously growing incisor teeth in each jaw and the ab-

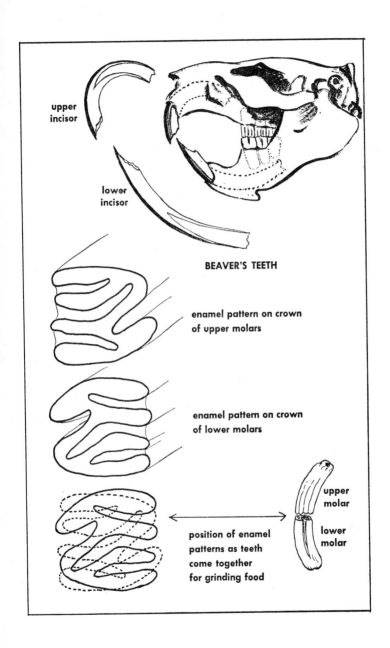

upper
incisor

lower
incisor

BEAVER'S TEETH

enamel pattern on crown
of upper molars

enamel pattern on crown
of lower molars

upper
molar

lower
molar

position of enamel
patterns as teeth
come together
for grinding food

sence of canines. With their amazingly developed incisors, rodents can gnaw, nip, and bite. Compared with the tapering root of a typical incisor, the broad, open root of a rodent's incisor is extremely long and grows from far back in the jawbone and skull. The thin layer of enamel on the front of the tooth is generally orange in color, and the exposed part of the tooth is less than half the length of the root section.

Rabbits are often mistakenly called rodents, but they belong to the order Lagomorpha, not to the order Rodentia, because they have four incisor teeth in the upper jaw and two in the lower. The extra incisors in the upper jaw grow directly behind the front ones, and they are much smaller in size. The little rock rabbit, or pika, also has the same rudimentary teeth growing in back of its upper incisors. In addition to these extra teeth, the structure of the larger front incisors is different from that of typical rodents' incisors. The rabbit's incisors have an enamel covering all around each tooth while rodents' are covered only on the front surface. The rabbit's molars are rootless and ever-growing.

Anyone who has attempted to capture a mouse or squirrel knows that he can be badly bitten if he holds the rodent in his hands. The incisor teeth of the smallest rodents are capable of inflicting deep and painful injuries, and almost all of these animals have the instinct to use their teeth when fighting or attempting to escape. Rabbits sometimes use their teeth when fighting among themselves, but for some reason they seldom, if ever, try to bite people or other animals. A friend of mine who has had much experience with beavers tells me that they rarely show any inclination to bite when handled by human beings. Nonetheless, I do not suggest putting hands on an adult wild beaver.

As a tool for cutting, the beaver's incisor tooth is quite remarkable. Like that of all rodents, it continues to grow as long as the animal lives. Its root remains broad and open, unlike the narrow root of most teeth, and it carries plenty of nourishment to the fast-growing tooth. It is estimated that a beaver's incisor tooth may grow at a rate of about four feet in a year. This rapid growth is necessary to replace the amount worn away at the tip, for the hard enamel is very thin and covers only the front of the tooth. The sides and back of the tooth are composed of relatively soft ivory, enabling the rodent to sharpen its own front teeth by chiseling the lowers against the uppers.

When an incisor tooth is damaged, a rodent is in grave trouble. If only a small part of the tooth is broken off, the damaged part is replaced by new growth. When an entire incisor breaks off close to the jaw, however, the opposite tooth in the other jaw no longer rubs against it and it may continue to grow in an arc until it circles back into the mouth.

Then the unfortunate rodent dies of starvation, because it cannot close its mouth to chew. The woodchuck seems to suffer this fate more frequently than other rodents, due perhaps to its habit of biting any object, no matter how hard it may be, when in danger. A frightened woodchuck will bite as viciously at an iron bar as it will at a dog's tender nose.

There is considerable difference in cheek teeth among rodents. Some, like the beaver's molars, are rootless and ever-growing, while those of the woodchuck have roots like typical teeth. The molars of a few rodents, like meadow mice, have zigzag patterns of enamel on the crown. Most others, however, have ridges of enamel running across their molars. This surface grinds food better when the animal moves its jaws forward and backward while chewing.

The patterns formed by the enamel on the crown of a rodent's cheek teeth are the same in the teeth of the upper and lower jaws. It is interesting to note, however, that the patterns are reversed, those on the teeth of the lower jaws being exactly the opposite of those on the teeth in the upper jaws. This arrangement creates a marvelous grinding apparatus, for the enamel ridges on the crowns of the upper teeth crisscross the ridges on the crowns of the lower teeth.

ANIMAL TEETH

POUCHED MAMMALS (MARSUPIALS)

Marsupials spend the early part of their life in their mother's pouch. Although they ranged over the whole world long ago, the opossum is the only marsupial found in America today. Australia has several, including kangaroos and koalas as well as a number of less familiar kinds of cats, mice, moles, and wolves.

The opossum has eighteen incisors, four canines, twelve premolars, and sixteen molars—fifty teeth in all. That number of teeth is considerably more than most flesh eaters and plant eaters have, but opossums eat both flesh and fruit, as well as eggs, and perhaps they need many different teeth to handle their varied diet.

An examination of the kangaroo's skull reveals some very strange teeth. In fact, the two lower incisors protrude directly forward almost like the lower incisors of a rodent. Opposing them in the upper jaw are six incisors of which the innermost pair are the largest and adapted for cutting. Through some curious development of its lower jaw, the kangaroo can move each lower incisor separately, which results in a scissorlike action as the two teeth move past one another. As far as I know, this instance is the only one in which the inside surface of an incisor tooth is used as a cutting edge.

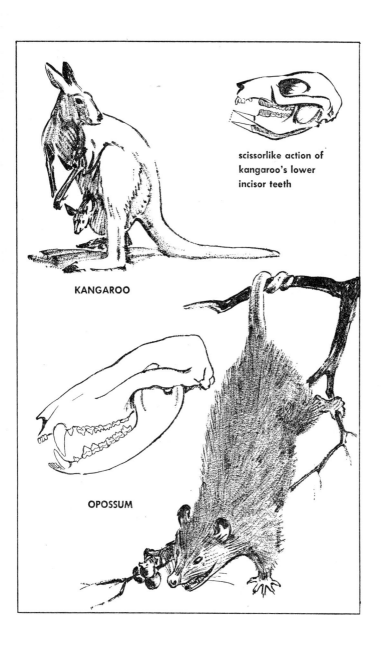

scissorlike action of
kangaroo's lower
incisor teeth

KANGAROO

OPOSSUM

MAMMAL TEETH

The only canines of the kangaroo are in the upper jaw, and they are small and practically useless. The cheek teeth appear to fit together as efficiently as those of other plant-eating animals, but the upper and lower front teeth are so different that they give the appearance of belonging to two entirely different species of animals.

Mammal teeth often resemble familiar tools, instruments, and weapons in their use and structure. The cheek teeth of carnivores may have sharp, shearing blades while those of herbivores work like grinders and millstones. The rodent's incisor teeth are efficient chisels, the kangaroo's lower incisors work like scissors, the vampire bat's upper incisors are keen-edged scalpels, and there are other mammal teeth comparable to awls, spears, hooks, or rakes. Each set of teeth is adapted to a mammal's eating habits and provides it with the tools it needs to obtain and eat its food.

FISH TEETH

In general, the function of a fish's teeth is to grip securely the slippery bodies of captured prey, but fish may have slashing and cutting teeth, rasping teeth, blunt crushing teeth, powerful nippers, and long beaks with saw teeth for other purposes.

The most obvious examples of teeth used primarily for slashing and cutting are found in the jaws of the piranha fish and several members of the shark family. The efficiency of the shark's sharp, serrated teeth has been demonstrated when these "wolves of the sea" bite huge chunks of blubber from the sides of dead whales during whaling operations at sea. Many sportsmen have been exasperated when they discover that a shark has bitten off half the body of a sailfish or tuna that they were attempting to land after a hard fight on rod and reel.

60

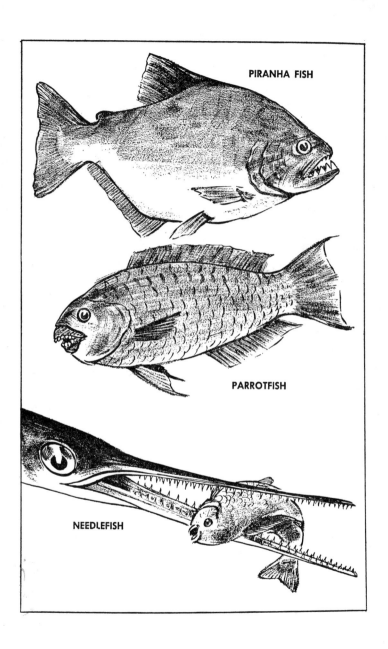

PIRANHA FISH

PARROTFISH

NEEDLEFISH

When compared to an adult man-eating shark, a piranha fish is insignificant in size; yet this little saber-toothed fish, although small enough to be kept in a household aquarium, is one of the most blood-thirsty fish in the world. Piranhas are fearless, and groups of them are quite capable of attacking, killing, and devouring a human being or an animal as big as a cow. When hundreds of these ferocious fish start tearing away bits of skin and flesh with their sharklike teeth, a large animal is reduced to a skeleton in a matter of minutes. Fortunately, piranha fish are not common; they are found only in some South American rivers.

Rasping teeth, such as those located on the tongues and in the mouths of the jawless hagfish and lampreys, are used to file holes through a fish's skin in order to suck the victim's blood. The hagfish has a single tooth in the roof of its mouth and two rows of toothlike plates on its tongue. The lamprey's rasping tools consist of a series of horny teeth scattered over the inside of its sucking mouth and on its tongue. Lampreys are toothless until they reach adulthood.

Fish that feed on crustaceans and coral need strong, blunt, or flattened teeth for crushing or grinding the hard outer skeletons of these sea animals. To perform this crushing and grinding operation, several kinds of fish have a second pair of jaws located in their throat. The jaws are equipped with strong pebblelike teeth, or teeth in the form of cubes and prisms arranged in mosaic patterns. Besides this "stone-crusher" apparatus, such fish as the sheepshead and parrotfish also have strongly developed front teeth in the upper and lower jaws, which can bite off chunks of coral or pick up crustaceans. Other fish having throat teeth are the carps, the porgie, and sea drum. The weird-looking, bat-winged skates and rays have flat, pavementlike teeth in their mouth instead of their throat. Certain species of skates are peculiar in that the male's teeth are sharp and pointed while those of the female are blunt and flattened.

Sawfish and sawsharks both have long, flat beaks with a row of teeth on each side. Thus armed, the beak is like a double-edged saw, and the fish uses it as a weapon. The sawfish, which grows to a length of more than fourteen feet, has strong teeth. It uses them by striking sideways through the water with such force that large fish have been known to cut bathers completely in two. The sawshark is a smaller fish with much smaller and sharper teeth, a smaller tooth alternating with each larger one.

If you look in the clear, blue water around the reefs and jetties along the Florida coast, there are usually some small, long-bodied needlefish to be seen swimming about. Their long, pointed beaklike jaws are armed their entire length with rows of small, sharp teeth. When hunting food, the needle-

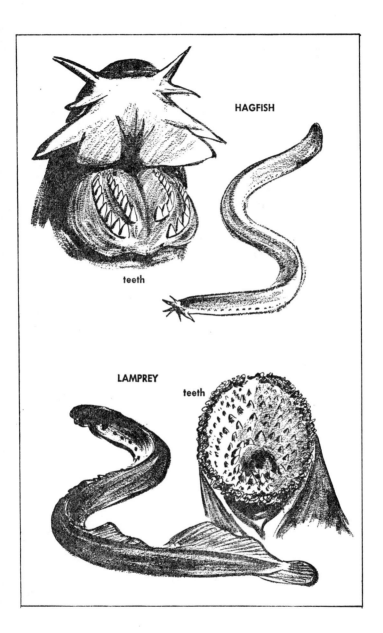

HAGFISH

teeth

LAMPREY

teeth

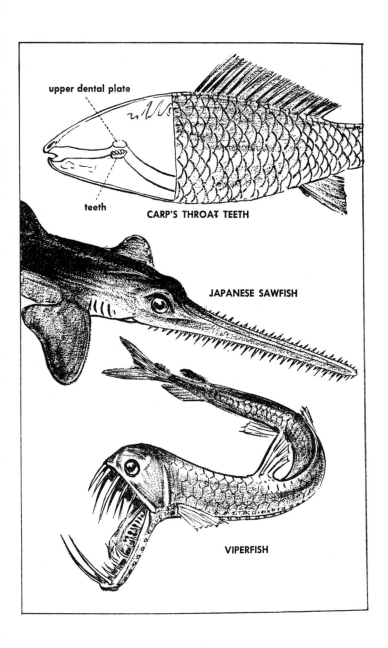

upper dental plate

teeth

CARP'S THROAT TEETH

JAPANESE SAWFISH

VIPERFISH

fish swims alongside its intended prey looking inno-
cent of any evil intentions. Then suddenly it side-
swipes with open mouth and grasps the victim in
its spike-studded jaws.

The unusual and extreme development of a viperfish's teeth is truly fantastic. This miniature hobgob-
lin, lurking in the darkened depths of the sea in-
habited by other small and strange-looking fish, has
an enormous mouth filled with so many long, stiletto-
like teeth that it would seem impossible for the fish
to close its mouth without stabbing its own jaws.
To add to the fierce appearance presented by the
teeth, the viperfish's mouth is lit up by luminous
patches that gleam inside the jaws. According to
the report of a scientist who dredged some of these
fish from the depths of the Mediterranean Sea, the
dreadful-looking teeth bend under pressure, but
they are strong enough to pierce the soft bodies of
their deep-sea victims.

Of all animals, fish have the greatest variety of
teeth. They range in number from zero to the thousands, and they are extremely varied in size and
shape and in their location in the mouth and on the
jaws. As a general rule, fish teeth are constantly being renewed throughout the animal's life, there being but a few species in which a single set lasts a
lifetime.

REPTILE TEETH

Many of the largest animals inhabiting the earth millions of years ago were reptiles, better known by most of us as dinosaurs. Of course, they are now extinct, and today living reptiles are limited to comparatively small and less frightening animals.

There is often some difficulty in distinguishing amphibians from reptiles. The most frequent error of identification is made when a salamander, which is an amphibian, is called a lizard, which is a reptile. It is easy to identify salamanders correctly, because lizards always have dry, scaly skin while the skin of salamanders and other amphibians is soft and scaleless. Frogs and toads are also amphibians.

The teeth are always small and pointed. Salamanders may have patches of teeth on the roof of their mouth, or palate, as well as rows on the rims

70

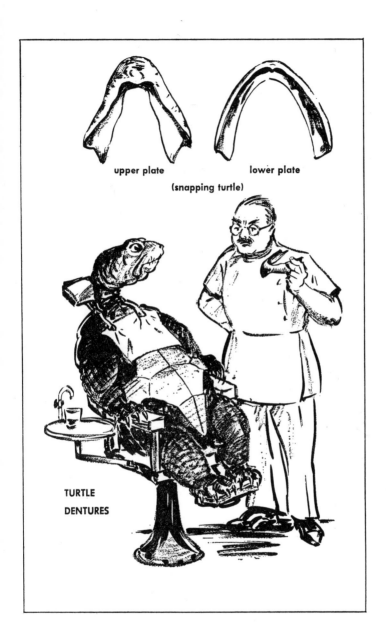

upper plate   lower plate

(snapping turtle)

TURTLE
DENTURES

of the upper and lower jaws, but frogs and toads seldom have any teeth in the lower jaw. In general, the teeth are adapted only to holding small prey, which is usually swallowed alive and whole.

Some kinds of reptiles and amphibians have a very specialized and temporary tooth. Egg-laying snakes, many lizards, and many frogs develop an egg tooth before they are hatched. This tooth enables the young to slash an opening in the tough shell when they are ready to hatch out, and they shed it shortly afterward.

Permanent reptile teeth are never implanted in the jaws by two or more roots, as mammal teeth are, and they are replaced continuously throughout life. There are no enfoldings of enamel on the crowns, and the teeth are adapted to gripping, killing, and tearing, but never to chewing or grinding food. Their teeth are not always confined to the margin of their jaws, but may be spread over the entire palate.

Crocodiles and alligators are the largest of our present-day reptiles. Their teeth are implanted in sockets along the margin of the jaws, but those of other reptiles are not. They are used solely for gripping their victims, which, if too large to swallow whole, may be torn into bits by the spinning action of the crocodile's body as it turns over in the water. There are from seventeen to twenty teeth on each side of the upper and lower jaws.

Turtles and tortoises have no teeth. Instead they

have sharp-edged horny plates on their jaws. Recently, on the sandy shore of a pond, I found the skull of a snapping turtle with the beak still attached to the jaws. When I picked it up, the upper and lower plates of the beak separated from the jawbones and fell to the ground. Much to my surprise, I discovered that the plates could be fitted back into the jawbones exactly like a set of teeth made by a dentist. Since then many of my friends have been greatly amused when I show them the turtle's dentures.

A lizard's teeth are attached to the bones of the jaws and, in some species, to the palate as well. There are many kinds of lizards, ranging in size from the tiny, lightning-fast fence lizards, which feed on worms and insects, to the slower-moving Komodo lizard, which is ten feet long and can swallow the hind-quarters of a pig in one gulp.

The Gila monster, which inhabits parts of Arizona and New Mexico, is a particularly interesting lizard. It is easily recognized by its thick, stubby tail and by the peculiar beaded texture of its pink- and black-banded skin. The bite of the Gila monster is dangerously poisonous to man and fatal to any small animal unfortunate enough to be seized in its powerful jaws. The venom in the form of toxic saliva enters the victim's bloodstream by means of grooved fangs in the lizard's lower jaw. As soon as it secures a firm grip on its prey and sinks its fangs into the

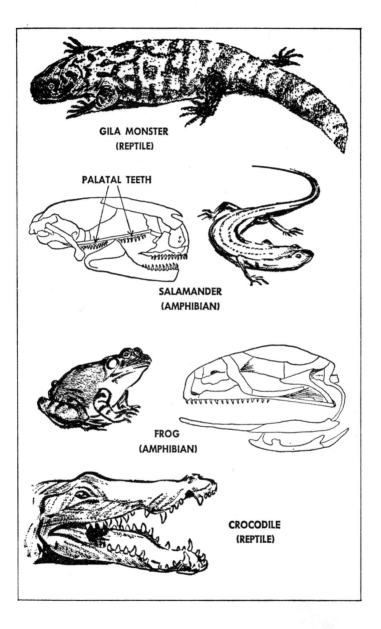

GILA MONSTER
(REPTILE)

PALATAL TEETH

SALAMANDER
(AMPHIBIAN)

FROG
(AMPHIBIAN)

CROCODILE
(REPTILE)

flesh, the Gila monster quickly turns over on its back and remains in that position long enough for the poisonous saliva to run down the grooved fangs into the wound. The act of turning over is puzzling. It doesn't seem possible that a lizard understands the law of gravity; nevertheless, it uses gravity to make its venom flow down into the fang wounds.

Some people dislike snakes, and perhaps one of the reasons is that their eating habits in many instances seem cruel. Because most nonpoisonous snakes capture and devour living animals, it is not uncommon to see the movements of the recently swallowed victim as it struggles in a snake's stomach. The snake's process of swallowing its living prey is a long drawn-out ordeal, because the victim is slowly pulled into the snake's expanding jaws and throat and down into the stomach to die of suffocation.

A small snake, with a body no more than a half inch in diameter, can easily swallow a much larger frog or bird. The snake's mouth can be stretched to several times its normal size, because the two branches of the lower jaw are connected at the chin by an elastic ligament that permits the two halves to expand outward. In addition, the bones of the upper jaw and palate are also connected by elastic ligaments, so they expand too. The jaws and the palate are provided with many sharp, recurved

77

teeth. When the snake seizes its prey, the jaws can stretch out wide enough to engulf the animal.

The stretchable ligaments permit the jaws to move forward and backward, which is the secret of the snake's ability to swallow its prey. As soon as an animal is captured, the upper and lower jawbones on *one side* of the snake's head move forward, the sharp, recurved teeth hook into the prey, and the jaws move backward, drawing the animal a short distance into the snake's mouth. Slowly, first on one side and then on the other, the jaws move forward and back forcing the animal into the throat, which is elastic enough to stretch and receive it.

Some big snakes, such as boas and pythons, kill their prey before swallowing it by coiling around the animal and crushing its body. Venomous snakes also kill their prey before swallowing it, but in a different way. Many poisonous snakes have movable tubular or grooved fangs on either side of the upper jaw. They are used like slender hypodermic needles to inject venom into the wounds they make. The fangs lie flat inside a protective sheath in the snake's mouth when it is closed, but the sheath is drawn back and they stand erect when the mouth is opened for striking. The venom, coming from glands in the snake's head, is forced through the hollow fangs by powerful muscles that exert pressure on the poison glands. The spitting cobra has an opening on the front side of each of its fangs and can squirt venom

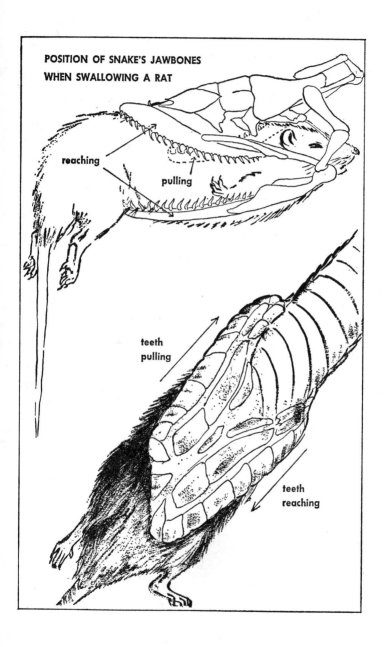

POSITION OF SNAKE'S JAWBONES
WHEN SWALLOWING A RAT

reaching

pulling

teeth
pulling

teeth
reaching

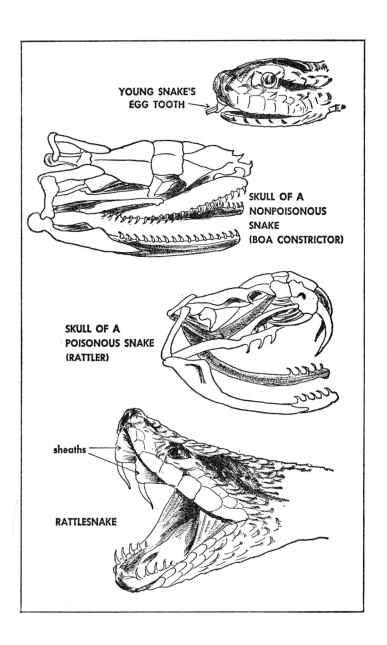

YOUNG SNAKE'S
EGG TOOTH

SKULL OF A
NONPOISONOUS
SNAKE
(BOA CONSTRICTOR)

SKULL OF A
POISONOUS SNAKE
(RATTLER)

sheaths

RATTLESNAKE

out of its mouth the way a boy can shoot water out of a water pistol, but the fangs of most other venomous snakes have their opening at the tip and shoot venom straight down into the wounds made by the fangs.

The long, slender fang is frequently broken off during use, but there are several others lying behind it to take its place. If venomous snakes were not able to replace broken fangs, they would probably die of starvation since they are in the habit of eating only the lifeless victims of their deadly poison.

The fang of the venomous snake is perhaps the most interesting of all reptile teeth, and it may well be the most deadly weapon found in the entire animal kingdom.

ARISTOTLE'S LANTERN

Animal teeth are so varied in number and structure that I find it difficult to single out one animal and say that it has the most interesting teeth. Perhaps, however, the dental apparatus of the little, spine-covered sea urchin, the simplest animal that has teeth for grinding food, is the most fascinating to me.

The jaws and teeth of the sea urchin can be easily removed in a unit for observation. When separated from the spine-covered dome, I defy anyone other than a zoologist to recognize the complete mechanism as an animal's jaws and dental equipment. Long ago someone gave me one of these marvelous creations, and I carried it around in a little glass bottle for some time before I learned that it was indeed Aristotle's Lantern and not part of a plant as I had suspected.

SEA URCHIN

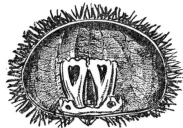

cross section
showing position
of jaws

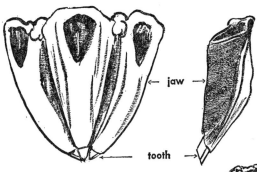

← jaw →

tooth →

ARISTOTLE'S LANTERN

teeth spread

ARISTOTLE'S LANTERN

The Greek philosopher, Aristotle, gave the sea urchin's jaws and teeth the name of Aristotle's Lantern, because he thought they looked like a lantern. I made a different comparison after I observed the mechanical features of the jaws. Tiny muscles acting as hinges hold the five jaw parts together. By gently spreading the parts, I opened the jaws outward in a manner that reminded me of the action of an excavator.

The sea urchin's intricate chewing apparatus consists of twenty principal parts all held together in a five-sided, cone-shaped mass. Each of the five sections has a single tooth at its lower point, and when the jaws are closed all five teeth come together at once. Instead of moving up and down, as most teeth do when chewing, they converge toward the center. Each tooth makes a grinding surface, and food is ground up as it passes among them. Only by seeing it and moving its parts, can anyone fully appreciate the structural beauty and mechanical precision of this marvelous little machine.

After studying the structure of all kinds of animal teeth, it is surprising to me that I found the most interesting dental apparatus in an animal that has no skull.

VOCABULARY

Canine—pointed tooth next to incisors

Carnassial teeth—last premolar of upper jaw and first molar of lower jaw

Carnivore—flesh eater

Cartilage—translucent, elastic tissue

Cartilaginous—made of cartilage

Cementum—a bonelike substance formed on the root and neck of mammal teeth

Cusp—a pointed end

Dentine—a hard, fine grained material, which composes the main part of a tooth

Dentition—the number, kind, and arrangement of teeth

Edentate—toothless (or almost toothless) animal

ANIMAL TEETH

Enamel—hard, outer layer of a tooth

Herbivore—grass and plant eater

Incisors—cutting teeth located in front of jaw

Insectivore—insect eater

Marsupial—pouched animal

Molars—cheek teeth behind premolars

Omnivore—animal that eats everything

Palate—roof of the mouth

Parts of a tooth:
    crown—upper surface
    cusp—a point on the crown
    unicuspid—one cusp
    biscuspid—two cusps
    tricuspid—three cusps
    nerve—inner pulp of root

Piscivore—fish eater

Placoid—scales bearing projecting spines

Premolars—teeth preceded by milk teeth

Recurved—points turned backward

Rudimentary—undeveloped

DENTITION OF MAMMALS

CARNIVORES

Badger
Mink
Skunk (common)
Weasel
$\}$ ············· $I\frac{3}{3}$, $C\frac{1}{1}$, $P\frac{3}{3}$, $M\frac{1}{2}$ = 17

Bear
Coyote
Dog
Fox
Wolf
$\}$ ················· $I\frac{3}{3}$, $C\frac{1}{1}$, $P\frac{4}{4}$, $M\frac{2}{3}$ = 21

Cat ············· $I\frac{3}{3}$, $C\frac{1}{1}$, $P\frac{2 \text{ or } 3}{2}$ $M\frac{1}{1}$ = 14 or 15

Hyena ················· $I\frac{3}{3}$, $C\frac{1}{1}$, $P\frac{4}{3}$, $M\frac{1}{1}$ = 17

ANIMAL TEETH

Land otter . . . . $I\frac{3}{3}$, $C\frac{1}{1}$, $P\frac{4}{3}$, $M\frac{1}{2}$ = 18

Pine marten⎱
Wolverine ⎰ . . . . $I\frac{3}{3}$, $C\frac{1}{1}$, $P\frac{4}{4}$, $M\frac{1}{2}$ = 19

Raccoon . . . . $I\frac{3}{3}$, $C\frac{1}{1}$, $P\frac{4}{4}$, $M\frac{2}{2}$ = 20

Sea otter . . . . $I\frac{3}{2}$, $C\frac{1}{1}$, $P\frac{3}{3}$, $M\frac{1}{2}$ = 16

Sloth bear . . . . $I\frac{2}{3}$, $C\frac{1}{1}$, $P\frac{4}{4}$, $M\frac{2}{3}$ = 20

Skunk (hog-nosed) . . . . $I\frac{3}{3}$, $C\frac{1}{1}$, $P\frac{2}{3}$, $M\frac{1}{2}$ = 16

HERBIVORES

Bison
Black-tailed deer
Caribou
Moose
Mountain sheep   ⎬ . . . . . $I\frac{0}{3}$, $C\frac{0}{1}$, $P\frac{3}{3}$, $M\frac{3}{3}$ = 16
Mule deer
Pronghorn antelope
Rocky Mountain goat
White-tailed deer

DENTITION OF MAMMALS

Hare
Rabbit $\Big\}$ .... $I\frac{2}{1}, C\frac{0}{0}, P\frac{3}{2}, M\frac{3}{3} = 14$

Horse .... $I\frac{3}{3}, C\frac{1}{1}, P\frac{3}{3}, M\frac{3}{3} = 20$

Pika .... $I\frac{2}{1}, C\frac{0}{0}, P\frac{3}{2}, M\frac{2}{3} = 13$

RODENTS

Beaver
Eastern chipmunk
Fox squirrel $\Big\}$ .... $I\frac{1}{1}, C\frac{0}{0}, P\frac{1}{1}, M\frac{3}{3} = 10$
Pocket gopher
Porcupine

Gray squirrel
Prairie dog $\Big\}$ .... $I\frac{1}{1}, C\frac{0}{0}, P\frac{2}{1}, M\frac{3}{3} = 11$
Red squirrel

Muskrat
Pack rat $\Big\}$ .... $I\frac{1}{1}, C\frac{0}{0}, P\frac{0}{0}, M\frac{3}{3} = 8$

Wapiti .... $I\frac{0}{3}, C\frac{1}{1}, P\frac{3}{3}, M\frac{3}{3} = 17$

MARSUPIALS

Kangaroo .... $I\frac{3}{1}, C\frac{0 \text{ or } 1}{0}, P\frac{1}{1}, M\frac{4}{4} = 14 \text{ or } 15$

Opossum .... $I\frac{5}{4}, C\frac{1}{1}, P\frac{3}{3}, M\frac{4}{4} = 25$